HOME
FOR THE
HOLIDAYS

Art by Charles Schulz

 bendon®  PEANUTS by SCHULZ

FINISH THE SLED.

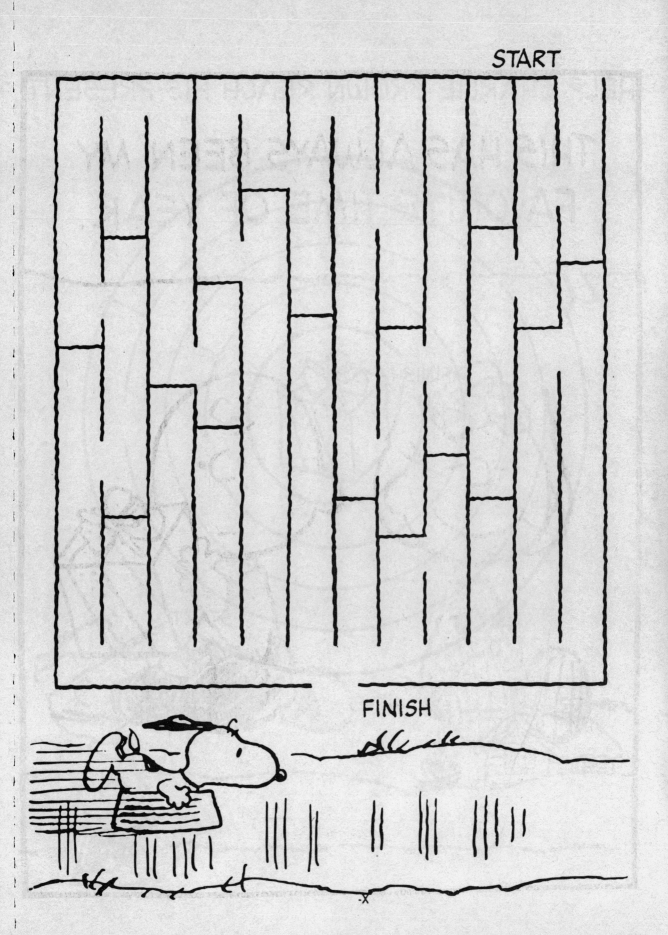

HELP CHARLIE BROWN REACH HIS PRESENT.

I built a
tumbleweed man!

DEAR SANTA

CHRISTMAS DOT-TO-DOT

CAN YOU FIND YOUR WAY DOWN THE HILL?

START

FINISH

HOW MANY WORDS CAN YOU MAKE FROM THE LETTERS IN:
SNOWMAN TIME

_____   _____

_____   _____

_____   _____

_____   _____

_____   _____

_____   _____

_____   _____

_____   _____

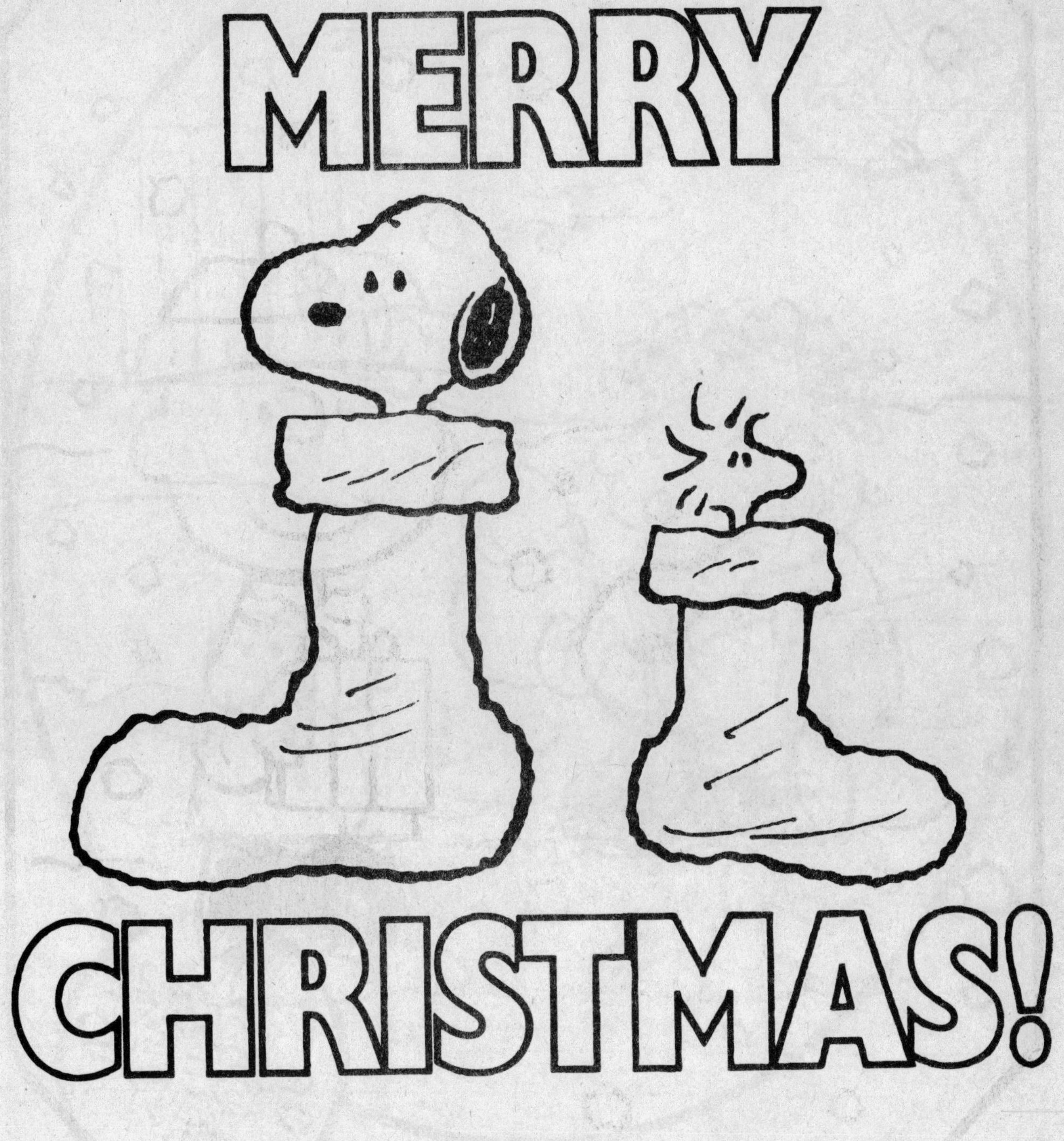
MERRY
CHRISTMAS!

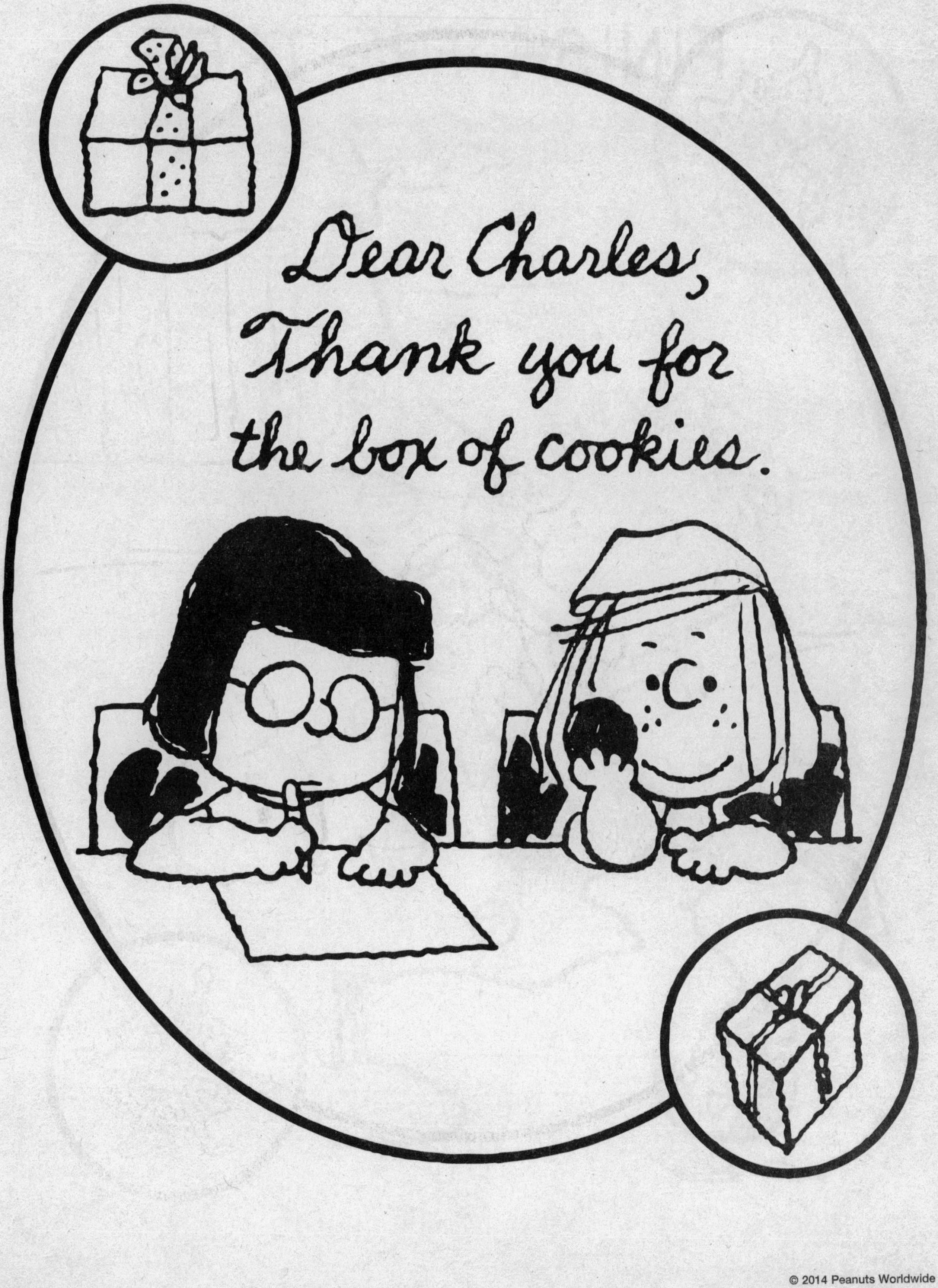
Dear Charles,
Thank you for
the box of cookies.

FINISH THE TREE.

CHRISTMAS DOT-TO-DOT

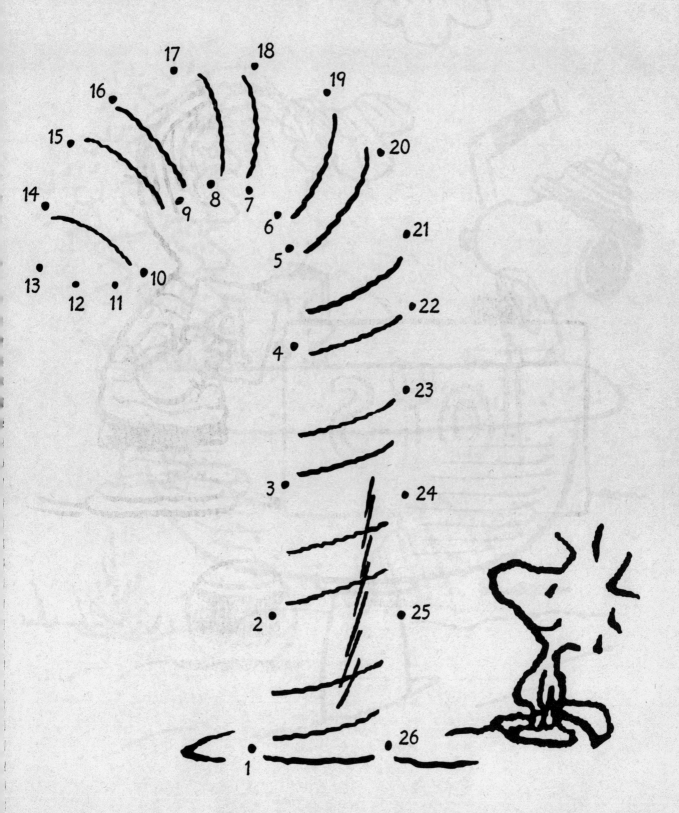

FIND YOUR WAY THROUGH THE MAZE.

START

FINISH

FINISH THE SNOWMAN.

MERRY CHRISTMAS!

HELP CHARLIE BROWN AND SALLY DECORATE THE CHRISTMAS TREE.

WAITING FOR SANTA

START

FINISH

HELP SANTA DOWN THE CHIMNEY TO DELIVER HIS GIFTS.

For my Christmas
tree, I decorated
a tumbleweed.

SEASON'S
GREETINGS!

HELP SNOOPY DECORATE HIS DOGHOUSE.

HOW MANY WORDS CAN YOU MAKE FROM THE LETTERS IN:
SNOWFLAKES

_____   _____

_____   _____

_____   _____

_____   _____

_____   _____

_____   _____

_____   _____

_____   _____

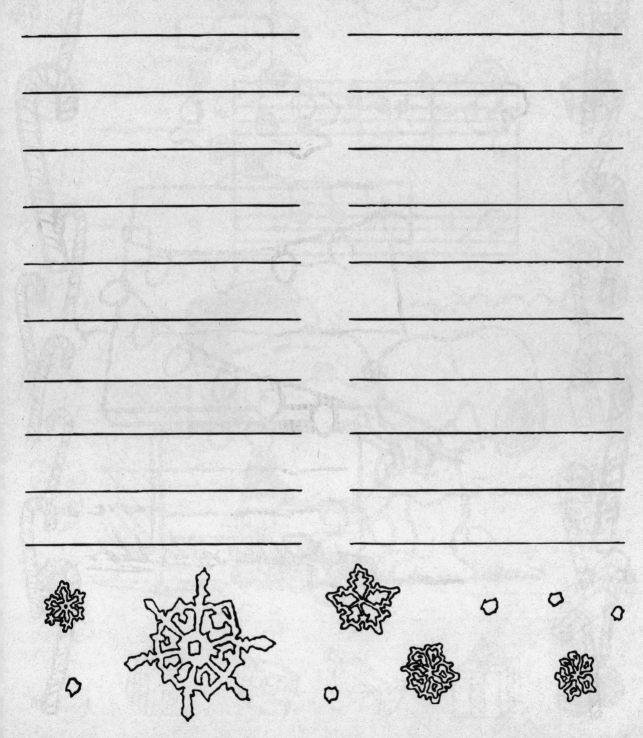

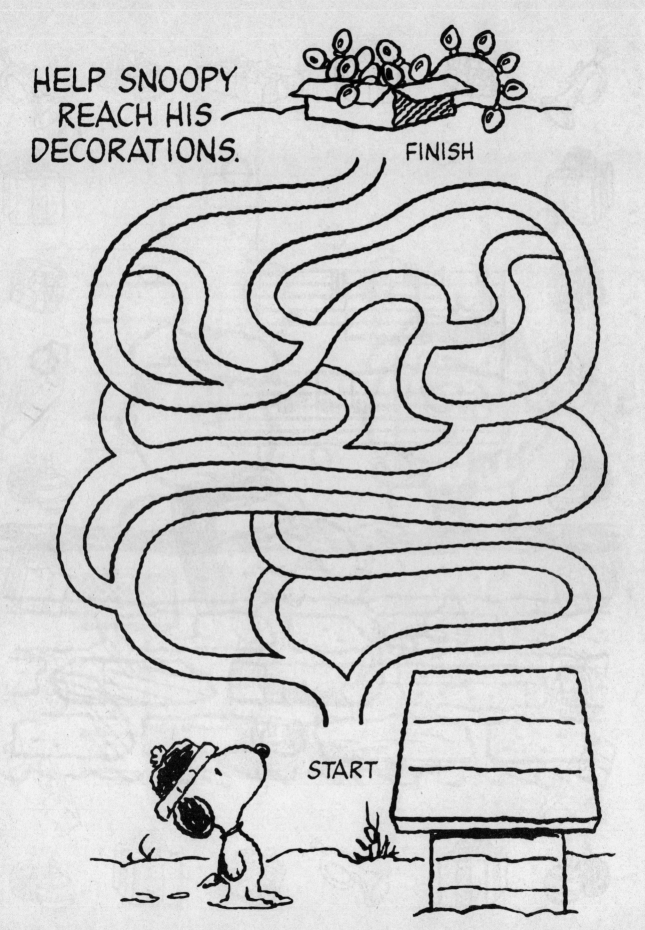

HELP SNOOPY REACH HIS DECORATIONS.

FINISH

START